DRAW TO CLOZE

Comprehension through reading and drawing exercises.

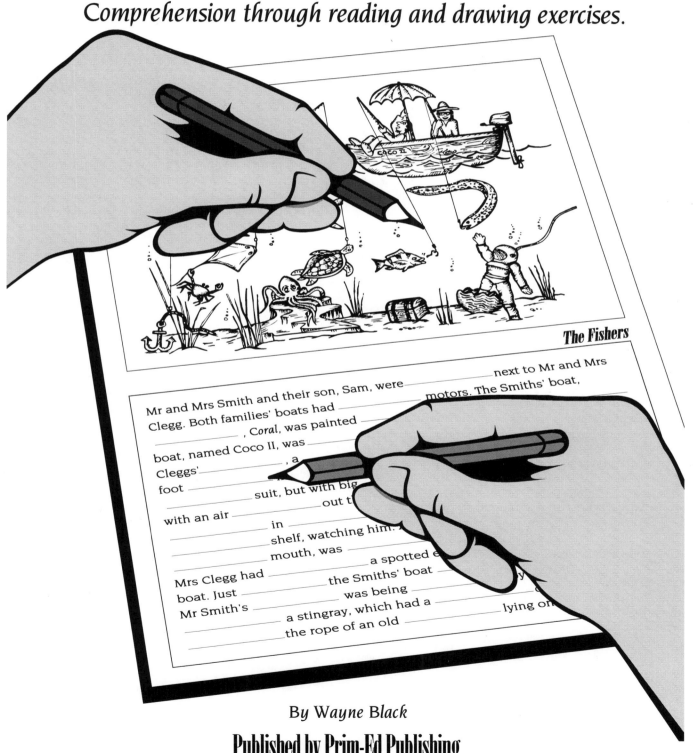

By Wayne Black

Published by Prim-Ed Publishing

M.J. SCOTT.

Middle and Upper

Draw to a
CLOZE

Comprehension through reading and drawing exercises

The Fishers

Mr and Mrs Smith and their son, Sam, were ———————— next to Mr and Mrs
Clegg. Both families' boats had ———————— motors. The Smiths' boat,
————————, *Coral*, was painted ————————
boat, named Coco II, was ————————
Cleggs' ————————, a
foot ———————— suit, but with big
———————— with an air ———————— out t
with an air ———————— in
———————— shelf, watching him.
———————— mouth, was ————————
Mrs Clegg had ———————— a spotted e
boat. Just ———————— the Smiths' boat ————————
Mr Smith's ———————— was being ————————
———————— a stingray, which had a ———————— lying on
———————— the rope of an old ————————

By Wayne Black

COPYRIGHT INFORMATION

ISBN 1-86400-289-1

9 781864 002898

Prim-Ed
Publishing

Draw to a Cloze
Prim-Ed Publishing

First published in 1995 by R.I.C. Publications
Reprinted under license in 1996 and 1997 by Prim-Ed Publishing

Copyright Wayne Black 1995

ISBN 1 86400 289 1
PR-0248

Prim-Ed Publishing Pty. Ltd.
Offices in: United Kingdom: PO Box 051, Nuneaton, Warwickshire, CV11 6ZU
               Australia: PO Box 332, Greenwood, Western Australia, 6024
               Republic of Ireland: PO Box 8, New Ross, County Wexford, Ireland

Foreword

Detailed drawings and interesting text make up this collection of comprehension activities.

Each picture-story provides the reader with two exercises.

First exercise: The reader is provided with complete text and shows comprehension by completing the accompanying picture.

Second exercise: The reader shows comprehension by completing a cloze task based on the accompanying picture.

There is opportunity in some activities for slightly varied answers or drawings. If the answer or drawing provided can be justified by the instruction then it should be seen as acceptable.

An opportunity to provide variety to your language programme. This form of comprehension provides an ideal indication of comprehension levels.

Contents

The Aliens

Foill and Beanh had returned from the visit to their moon. The moon could be seen high in the sky, above the clouds. As Foill descended the steps, the power-unit, located on the underside of the spaceship, was flashing green and yellow. Foill's spacesuit fitted her like a coat of orange paint. Her friend, Geinh, stood on the hover-sledge and held the handle. From the power-pads under the sledge, thin yellow thrust-beams drove into the ground. The two service robots hovered under the spaceship. Beanh, inside the ship, held a lever on the ceiling. This lever controlled the three bands of red and green light balls about the control room window. The wall behind Beanh had fifteen dials.

The Aliens

Foill and Beanh had returned _____ the visit to _____ moon.

The moon could be _____ high in the _____, above the

_____. The power-unit, located on the underside of the _____-

was _____ green and yellow as Foill descended the _____.

Foill's _____ fitted her like a _____ of orange paint. Her

friend, Geinh, _____ on the hover-sledge and _____ the

handle. From the power-pads _____ the sledge, thin yellow thrust-

beams _____ into the _____. The two _____ robots

_____under the spaceship. Beanh, _____ the ship,

_____ a lever on the ceiling. This _____ controlled the three

_____ of red and green _____ balls about the _____

room window. The wall _____ Beanh had _____ dials.

The Forest

The stream flows with blue water. Silver and gold pebbles dot the pool, and clumps of ferns stand along the stream's bank. The crack in the big tree is dark except for the eyes of a big animal hiding there. Some bones lie in front of this tree. A hedgehog is backed into the crack in the leaning tree. A mouse family hides between the roots of the tree. There are three owls about. One sits on the branch over the pool. It has a fledgling in a hole in the tree's trunk. In the tree to the left, another owl is in a hole. A fox stands in the clearing in the middle of the forest. A snake is coiled around the branch of a tree deeper in the woods. There are many spotted toadstools and flowers on the ground.

The Forest

The stream _____ with blue _____. Silver and gold pebbles

dot the pool, and clumps of _____ stand _____ the stream's

bank. The _____ in the big tree is dark, except for the _____ of

a big _____ hiding there. Some _____ lie in front of

_____ tree. A_____ is backed into the _____ in the

leaning tree. A mouse family _____ between the roots of the

_____. There are _____ owls about. One _____on

the branch over the pool. It has a fledgling in a _____ in the tree's

_____. In the _____ to the left, another owl is in

a_____. A_____ stands in the clearing in the middle of

the_____. A snake is _____around the _____ of a

tree deeper in the woods. There are many spotted _____and flowers on

the _____.

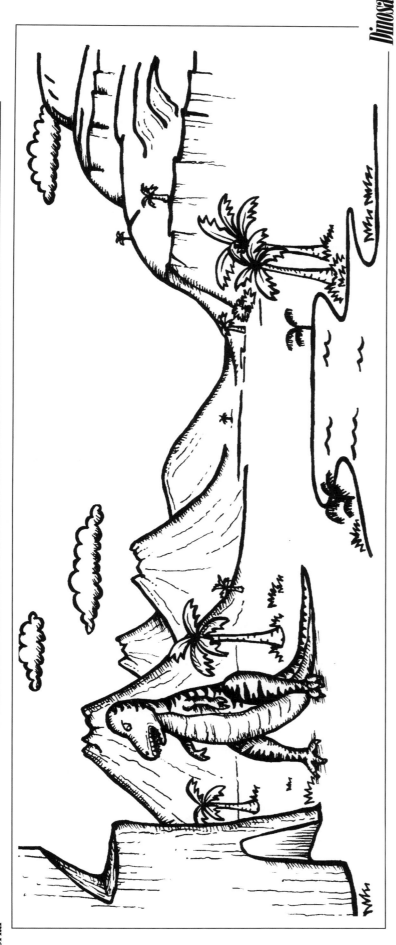

Doctor Xon had developed his time-scan machine. It sketched scenes of long ago. The machine was set for the 'Age of the Dinosaurs'. A huge *Tyrannosaurus Rex* was hunting a stegosaur, which was running to a cave. A triceratops followed the stegosaur, ready to fight the vicious T-Rex. On a ledge above the cave, was a nest of sticks. An egg lay in it.

Over in the swamp, an apatosaur, with only its head and neck poking out of the water, watched the other dinosaurs. It was not interested in the ferns around the swamp's edge or the other *Tyrannosaurus Rex* which stood over to the right and snarled angrily.

Above the valley, two pterodactyls flew towards their nest. Suddenly, a volcano erupted! Ash billowed skyward.

Doctor Xon had _____ his time-scan machine. It _____ scenes of long ago. The machine _____

set for the 'Age of the _____'. A huge *Tyrannosaurus* _____ was _____ a stegosaur, which was

_____ to a cave. A triceratops _____ the stegosaur, ready to _____ the vicious T-Rex. On a ledge

_____ the cave, was a _____ of sticks. An egg _____ in it. Over in the swamp, an _____

_____, with only its _____ and neck poking out of the _____, watched the _____

dinosaurs. It _____ not interested in the ferns _____ the swamp's edge or the _____

Tyrannosaurus Rex which stood over to the _____ and _____ angrily. Above the valley, _____

pterodactyls flew towards their _____. Suddenly, a _____ erupted! Ash _____ skywards.

This is where we laid out our picnic basket. We had lots of food, including sandwiches and pies on plates, and drinks in cups. In the hole in the tree trunk, we found an owl. There was also an ant nest in it. The ants came down in a line to the blanket to take bits of our cake. In the distance, you can see Sharon with her kite.

Near where we ate, there was a stream and a tree with a swing. Aunty Bab was floating on a rubber ring and I swung out over her. Oh wow! Did she scream! My little sister crawled out to the end of the branch and sat there, dangling her feet. Dad did not want to swim, so he sat on the edge with his feet in the water.

Uncle Steve took this just before we left to come home. Two hedgehogs were crossing in front of the car, and an ostrich had suddenly stuck its head and neck in towards Dad on the passenger's side. That's Mum behind the steering wheel, waving to Uncle Steve. You can see me, in between them, but in the back seat. We had the rubber ring and the picnic basket, tied down on the roof.

This is where we laid out our _____ basket. We had lots of food, including _____ and pies on plates, and _____ in cups. In the _____ in the tree trunk, we _____ an owl. There was also an ant nest in it, and the _____ came down in a _____ to take bits off our _____ on the _____. You can see Sharon _____ her kite in the distance.

Near _____ we ate, there was a _____ and a tree with a _____. Aunty Bab was floating on a _____ ring and I _____ out over her. Oh wow! Did she scream! My little sister _____ out to the end of the _____ and sat there, _____ her feet. Dad did not want to swim, so he _____ on the _____ with this feet in the _____.

Uncle Steve took this just before we left to _____ home. Two _____ were _____ in front of the car, and an ostrich had suddenly _____ its head and _____ in towards Dad on the passenger's side. That's Mum _____ the _____ wheel, waving to Uncle Steve. You can _____ me, in between them, but in the _____ seat. We had the _____ ring and the picnic _____ tied down on the _____.

Pictorial

The Cavern

You are exploring a cave. You climb over a pile of boulders that nearly block the cave's mouth. In the first chamber, you find

bones all over the floor and the ceiling covered in hanging bats. You climb down a rope to a chamber below. Stalactites

cling to the roof and stalagmites grow from the floor, like spikes. You crawl along a tunnel full of lizards and striped spiders.

You climb up a crack, full of sharp rocks, to a higher chamber. A coiled spotted snake, near its tunnel, watches you. Some

birds have built nests on ledges across from the snake. The last chamber is flooded. A bucket, from a well built above the

roof, floats on the water. Some frogs swim there.

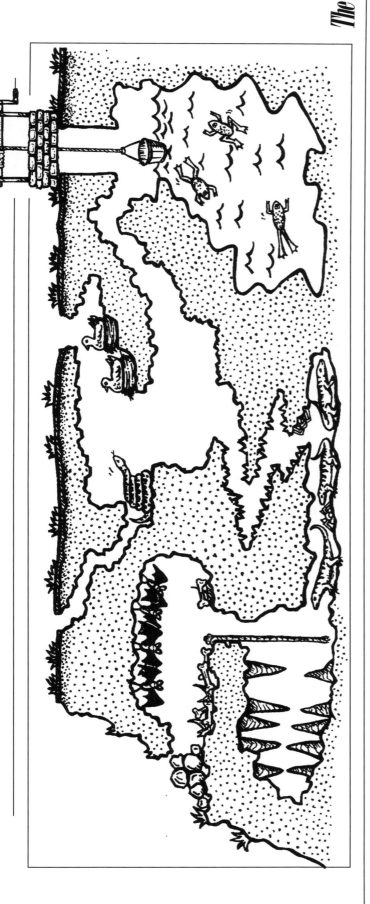

You are exploring a cave. You _____ over a pile of _____ that nearly block the cave's _____. In the first chamber, you find _____ all over the floor and the _____ covered in hanging _____. You _____ down a rope to a _____ below. Stalactites _____ to the roof and stalagmites _____ from the floor, like spikes. You _____ along a tunnel full of _____ and _____ spiders. You _____ up a crack, full of sharp _____, to a higher chamber. A coiled spotted _____ near its tunnel, watches you. Some _____ have built _____ on ledges _____ from the snake. The _____ chamber is flooded. A bucket, from a _____ built _____ the roof, _____ on the _____ water. Some frogs _____ there.

Pictorial

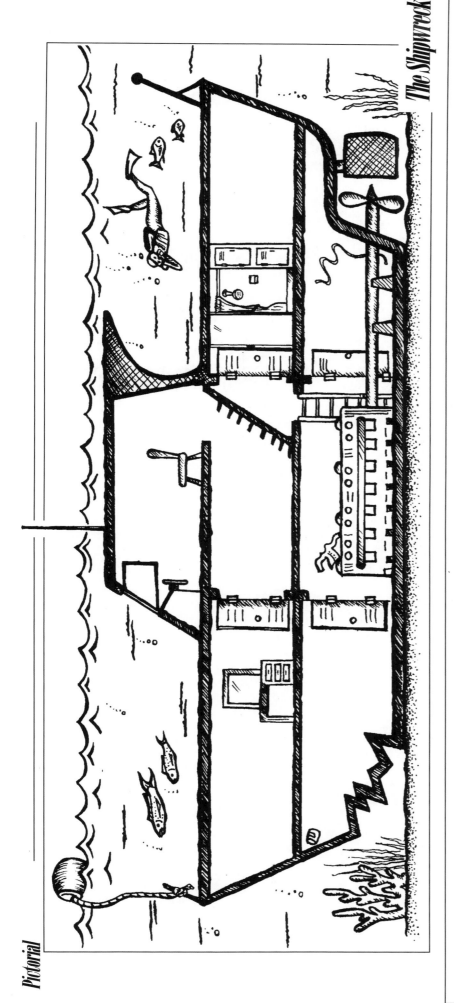

The diver explores the sunken ship and sees all kinds of things. The wreck is marked by a pennant on the mast above the water. A barrel buoy floats above the bow. It is tied to the bow by a rope. In the bridge cabin, there is a table and chair. An armchair is near the helm. A radio panel, with lots of dials, is on the wall. Down the stairs, the diver finds the galley. There is a long table and bench, and a cupboard with plates and pots and mugs on the wall. The bow cabin has a big bed, a mirrored dressing table and chair, and a long painting on the wall. The diver swims to the stern cabin and finds a shower and toilet closet, some double bunks and a wardrobe. On the bottom deck, she finds ropes, tins, boxes and clothes floating everywhere. In the bow compartment, an octopus has hold of a fish. A crab hangs off the door.

The Shipwreck

The diver explores the sunken ship and sees all kinds of things. The wreck is marked by a _____ on the mast above the _____. A barrel buoy _____ above the bow. It is _____ to the bow by a _____. In the bridge cabin, there is a table and _____. An armchair is _____ the helm. A _____ panel, with lots of dials, is on the _____. Down the stairs, the diver _____ the galley. There is a long _____ and bench, and a _____ with plates and pots and _____ on the wall. A stove is _____ behind the _____. The bow cabin _____ a big bed, a mirrored dressing _____ and a long painting on the wall. The diver _____ to the stern cabin and _____ a closet, some double _____ and a wardrobe. On the _____ deck, she _____ floating everywhere. In the bow compartment, an _____ has _____ ropes, tins, boxes and _____ off the door. A crab _____ hold of a fish.

Witch's Cottage

Nhaam, the elf, had sneaked into the home of Wart-nose, the evil witch, to find his friend that she had caught. First, he searched upstairs. He found two frogs there. One was under a table, which had a glass jar full of butterflies on it. The other was under Wart-nose's bed. The bedhead had a bat picture on it. A candle in the room burned with a green flame, which made an oval mirror on the wall glow green. The mirror had eyes and a mouth. It whispered that Nhaam should read two big books called *Spells* and *Potions*, but Nhaam didn't have the time. He went downstairs and hid behind a blue jar. He saw his friend was locked inside a hanging birdcage. Wart-nose was busy casting a spell on a rabbit she had on a stool. The rabbit had been turned blue, the same colour as Wart-nose's robe, with little yellow stars. Nhaam had a rescue plan. He would throw the purple, yellow and green jars, from the shelf above him, into the burning fireplace. Then, in the smoke, he would free his friend and they would escape through the mouse hole under the table.

Witch's Cottage

Nhaam, the elf, had sneaked into the _____ of Wart-nose, the
_____ witch, to _____his friend that she had caught. First,
he _____ upstairs. He _____ two frogs there. One was
_____ a table, which had a glass jar full of _____ on it. The
other was _____ Wart-nose's bed. The bedhead had a bat
_____ on it. A candle in the room _____ with a green
_____, which made an oval _____ on the wall glow green.
The mirror had _____ and a _____. It _____ that
Nhaam should _____ two big books _____ *Spells* and *Potions*,
but Nhaam didn't _____ the time. He went _____ and hid
_____a blue jar. He saw that his _____ was _____
inside a hanging _____. Wart-nose was busy _____ a spell
on a _____ she had on a _____. The rabbit had been
_____ blue, the same _____ as Wart-nose's robe, with little
_____ stars. Nhaam had a rescue _____. He would throw
the purple, yellow and green _____, from the shelf _____
him, into the _____ fireplace. Then, in the _____, he would
free his _____and they would _____ through the
_____ hole under the table.

Folks say the lighthouse on Rocks End is haunted. They say the ghosts of dead keepers stay there. On stormy nights, the lamp glows green and the ghost of a man, who fell from the top, hangs from the railing. Visitors to the top room have seen a glowing skeleton there. It seems to work the switches of the lamp motor. At times, the motor is surrounded by a reddish glow. In the bedroom, a wispy ghost in long, striped men's pyjamas often appears. This ghost throws clothes about the room. The kitchen holds the ghost of a big, bearded man. This ghost always has a coffee mug in his hand. When he appears, smoke comes out of the stove's chimney. Visitors hate the storeroom. It is always shadowy. Often, red, beady eyes with nasty sharp teeth seem to look over the lids of the boxes. There is always yellow fog on the ground floor. A sailor's ghost stands behind the entrance door.

Folks say the _____ on Rocks End is haunted. They say the ghosts of _____ keepers stay there. On stormy nights, the lamp _____ green and the ghost of a man, who _____ from the top, hangs from the _____. Visitors to the top room have seen a glowing _____ there. It seems to _____ the switches of the _____ motor. At _____ , the motor is surrounded by a reddish glow. In the _____, a wispy _____ in long, striped men's pyjamas often appears. This _____ throws clothes about the room. The kitchen _____ the ghost of a big, bearded man. This _____always has a coffee mug in his _____. When he appears, smoke _____ out of the stove's _____. Visitors hate the storeroom. It _____ always shadowy. Often, red beady _____ with nasty, sharp _____ seem to look over the lids of the _____. There is always yellow fog on the ground floor. A sailor's _____ stands behind the entrance _____.

Asteroid

Astronaut Seacal landed the spaceship carefully on the unknown asteroid's surface. The spaceship's tail glowed red with heat, like the walls of a gigantic crack that ran along the asteroid's surface. Black smoke and yellow sparks erupted from two volcanoes behind the spaceship, and red lava poured from the first into the huge crack. In the sky, two half-moons could be seen. Seacal put a ladder from the door to the surface, and then set up a camp site in front of a nearby crater. The camp had an igloo-like shelter, a small four-wheeled buggy and a flag on a pole. On the plain between the two mountain ranges, Seacal set up a three-legged radio dish. It was then the monsters appeared. From each of the four craters beyond the crack, a huge worm creature stuck up its head. Each head had three eyes on stalks, one nostril and a mouth full of triangular teeth!

Asteroid

Astronaut Seacal landed the _____ carefully on the unknown asteroid's

surface. The spaceship's tail _____ red with heat, like the walls of a

_____ crack that _____ along the asteroid's surface. Black

_____ and yellow sparks _____ from two _____

behind the spaceship, and red lava _____ from the first into the huge

crack. In the _____, two half- _____ could be seen. Seacal

_____ a ladder from the _____ to the surface and then

_____ up a camp site in _____ of a nearby crater. The camp

had an igloo-like _____ , a small _____-wheeled buggy and a

flag on a _____. On the plain _____ the two mountain

ranges, Seacal set up a three-legged _____ dish. It was then the

monsters _____. From each of the four _____ beyond the

crack, a huge worm _____ stuck up its head. Each _____ had

three eyes on stalks, _____ nostril and a mouth full of _____

teeth!

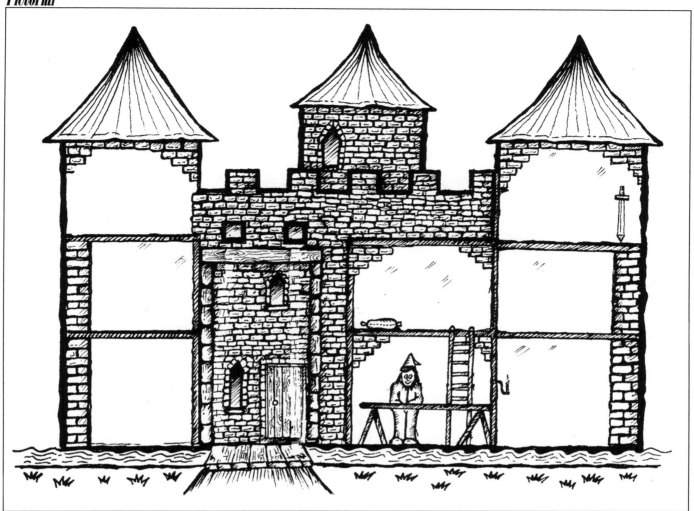

The Castle

The drawbridge is across the water-filled moat. The drawbridge is worked by chains through square holes in the wall. To the right of the entrance is a shop. Behind the shopkeeper is a shelf with jars and sacks of grain. There is an apple barrel on the floor. In the room above, there are four baskets and three sacks of grain. In the right tower of the castle, the ground floor room is a kitchen. There is a fireplace, a table and chair, and some pots and pans on the wall. The first floor is a parlour room. A lady sits knitting there. The top floor room is for weapons. There are swords, spears and bows and arrows along the wall. There is a guard standing on the battlement. In the left tower, the top room is a bed chamber. The room below is one also. The bottom chamber is a parlour room. There are two chairs in it. Each room in the castle has a candle in a holder on the wall.

The Castle

The drawbridge is across the _____-filled moat. The_____ is
worked by _____ through _____ holes in the _____.
To the right of the _____ is a shop. Behind the shopkeeper is a
_____ with jars and _____ of grain. There is an apple barrel
on the _____. In the room above, there are _____ baskets and
_____ sacks of _____. In the right tower of the castle, the
ground floor room is a _____. There is a _____, a table
and_____, and some pots and pans on the wall. The _____
floor is a parlour room. A _____ sits knitting _____. The top
floor room is for _____. There are _____, spears and bows and
_____ along the wall. There is a _____ standing on the
battlement. In the _____ tower, the top _____ is a bed
chamber. The room below is one _____. The bottom _____ is
a parlour _____. There are two _____ in it. Each room in the
_____ has a candle in the holder on the _____.

Volcano

The volcano had been dormant for many years, but now it was active. Blackish-grey smoke billowed from the red, glowing crater. A lava stream oozed down the side from a crack in the rim. Its heat had lit a hut and trees at the base. The villagers had to abandon their homes. Women carried baskets on their heads and children carried chickens, while the men herded the village's pigs. In the swamp, a crocodile floated near the centre and watched a water buffalo near the water's edge. Halfway up the track to the volcano's summit, three scientists were walking. They had backpacks. Their jeep was parked down the bottom, at the start of the track. In the sky, a news helicopter hovered near the edge of the crater. A video camera hung below the helicopter. Small eruptions from the volcano sent orange sparks, like little 'shooting stars', whizzing past the helicopter. Close call!

Volcano

The volcano had been dormant for _____ years, but now it was active.
Blackish-grey smoke _____ from the red, glowing crater. A lava stream
_____ down the side from a _____ in the rim. Its
_____ had lit a hut and trees at the base. The villagers had to
_____ their homes. _____ carried baskets on their
_____ and children _____ chickens, while the men
_____ the village's pigs. In the _____, a crocodile floated
near the _____ and watched a _____ buffalo near the water's
edge. Halfway up the _____ to the volcano's summit, _____
scientists were _____. They _____ backpacks. Their jeep was
_____ down the bottom, at the _____ of the track. In the sky,
a news _____ hovered near the edge of the _____. A video
_____ hung _____ the helicopter. Small eruptions from the
_____ sent orange sparks, like little 'shooting stars' _____
past the helicopter. Close call!

The Fishers

Mr and Mrs Smith and their son, Sam, were fishing next to Mr and Mrs Clegg. Both families' boats had outboard motors. The Smiths' boat, named *Coral*, was painted green and red. The Cleggs' boat, named *Coco* II, was painted gold and purple. Under the Cleggs' boat, a diver was standing on the seafloor with his foot caught in a giant clam. He looked like an astronaut in the diving suit, but with big metal boots and a helmet with an air hose out the back of it. There was an old treasure chest in front of him. A mottled octopus sat on a rock shelf, watching him. A fat, flat green fish with a huge mouth was nibbling at Mr Clegg's worm bait. Mrs Clegg had hooked a spotted eel, almost as long as the boat. Just beneath the Smiths' boat lurked a long, mean shark. Mr Smith's bait was being nibbled by a turtle. Mrs Smith had hooked a stingray, which had a crab on its tail. Sam had hooked the rope of an old anchor lying on the sand.

The Fishers

Mr and Mrs Smith and their son, Sam, were _____ next to Mr and Mrs Clegg. Both families' boats had _____ motors. The Smiths' boat, _____, *Coral*, was painted _____ and red. The _____ boat, named *Coco* II, was _____ gold and _____. Under the Cleggs' _____, a _____ was standing on the seafloor with his foot _____ in a giant clam. He looked like an astronaut in the _____ suit, but with big _____ boots and a _____ with an air _____ out the back of it. There was an old treasure _____ in _____ of him. A _____ octopus sat on a _____ shelf, watching him. A fat, flat _____ fish with a _____ mouth, was _____ at Mr Clegg's _____ bait. Mrs Clegg had _____ a spotted eel, almost as _____ as the boat. Just _____ the Smiths' boat _____ a long, mean shark. Mr Smith's _____ was being _____ by a turtle. Mrs Smith had _____ a stingray, which had a _____ on its tail. Sam had _____ the rope of an old _____ lying on the sand.